a

Amsterdam · Antwerpen
Em. Querido's Uitgeverij BV
2011

Translated by
**David Colmer**

www.queridokinderboeken.nl
www.annie-mg.com
www.anniemgschmidt.nl

Design Irma Boom

The illustrator received a grant for this work from the Netherlands
Foundation for Visual Arts, Design and Architecture (Fonds BKVB).

ISBN 978 90 451 1290 9
NUR 290

**Annie M.G. Schmidt's**
Most Beautiful Children's Poems
**Sieb Posthuma**
Illustrations

# A Pond
# Full of Ink

**The Man Who Writes Fairy Tales**

A fairy tale author I know
starts work every day when the roosters crow.

He writes very quickly, he writes without hitches
about fairies and elves and hobgoblins and witches.

He writes about princes, princesses and kings,
and keeps going till six when the dinner bell rings.

The next morning he's back when the sky's turning blue.
An inkpot's too little, so what does he do?

At the foot of his garden there's a pond full of ink.
The blackbirds all gather around it to drink.

And whenever that writer's at a loose end,
he goes down to that pond to refill his pen.

He's made up ten thousand stories already,
and has plenty more – he's constant and steady.

And if he keeps writing till the day that he dies,
perhaps he'll have written that pond of his dry.

## Nice and Naughty

I've had enough! I'm not a lamb!
I don't want to say hello!
I don't want to say, 'Yes, sir,' – 'Yes, ma'am,'
or hear about how big I am...
as if I didn't know.
I'll stay out in the yard all day
until I'm sure they've gone away!

I don't want to eat that mushy rice,
I don't want to brush my hair!
I don't want to hear their good advice.
I want to be naughty, not nice,
and lean back on my chair,
and play pirates in the kitchen sink,
and finger-paint with Indian ink!

And when it rains I'll go and dance
in puddles up to my knees.
I'll poke my tongue out at my aunts,
'cause when I'm old I'll have a chance
to say thank you and please.
And I'll do everything that's wrong,
the whole day long, the whole day long!

I want to jump on the settee
and cover it with grime.
I want to scream hysterically,
and take the dog to bed with me...
but I'll say when it's time.
That's all the things I plan to do.
If they don't like it, I'll say, 'Poo!'

## Three Elderly Otters

Three elderly otters longed to go boating
out on the river,
out on the moat.
For years, they had wished they could be out
    there floating,
but, being otters, they couldn't help noting,
signs on the seats of every last boat.
Written by renters, the miserable rotters,
they said…
FORBIDDEN FOR OTTERS

Three elderly otters standing there crying
there by the river,
there by the moat.
Crying and weeping and finally sighing,
'Maybe the train is fun and worth trying.'
But stuck in each window they spied a small
    note
that had them howling with their heads bowed.
It said…
OTTERS NOT ALLOWED

Three elderly otters, tired and spent,
leaving the river
and moat far behind,
saw in a meadow next to a tent
a big row of bicycles ready to rent,
and hung from each handlebar was a small sign
that made their day and what did it say?
It said...
OTTERS DON'T NEED TO PAY

Now the otters ride over the dyke,
over the dyke and back on their bikes.

## The Singing Tea Kettle

Their father's gone out and their mother's gone out,
the children are out and nobody's about,
the kettle is on the gas ring,
hear it sing, hear it sing, hear it sing: toooot.

The pan full of cabbage says, 'Bah, shame on you!
Why must you kick up such a hullabaloo?
I usually couldn't care less,
but you sound like the Orient Express!'

The casserole dish full of gravy and steak
says, 'Heavens to Betsy!' and 'Give us a break!
There's someone here trying to braise.
I've never braised worse all my days!'

The kettle laments, 'It's not me! It's not me!
My whistle's to blame for it all, don't you see?
Whenever I boil, it sings.
I can't stop it doing its thing!'

The parents and children still haven't come back,
the kettle is boiling and blowing its stack.
It sings and it sings like before.
We really can't stand anymore... Can you?

**Brian Brinck**

'Hello, Mrs Hughes,
have you heard the news?
Brian Brinck
from the ice-skating rink
left the tap running in the sink.
It ran for an hour and a quarter.
The kitchen was all under water.
Can you imagine the scene?
He'd just had it cleaned.
Tsk, tsk, tsk.'

'Hello, Mrs Glossop,
have you heard the gossip?
Brian Brinck
from the ice-skating rink
left the tap running in the sink.
It ran for a day and a half.
The house was as full as a bath.
Just imagine the mess!
Chairs were floating, no less.'

'Hello, Mrs Faye,
have you heard what they say?
Brian Brinck
from the ice-skating rink
left the tap running in the sink.
Six weeks unabated,
the whole street was inundated.
Just imagine the mess!
Cars were floating, no less.'

'Hello, Mrs Rafter,
have you heard 'bout the disaster?
Brian Brinck
from the ice-skating rink
left the tap running in the sink.
Five months unabated,
the whole town was inundated.
Just imagine it: *five*!
No one survived!'

'Look, is that who I think?
Brian Brinck from the ice-skating rink.
Brian, you're such a careful chap.
Why'd you leave the tap
running in the sink?'
'Oh,' said Brian, 'not for long.
The stories they tell are all wrong.
Just a splash, nothing more,
bit of water on the floor
–'bout a cup –
mopped it up,
got it done in a wink,'
said Brian Brinck.

With disappointment all around,
the ladies soon were homeward bound.

**The Furniture**

'Would you like to come out walking?' said the table to the chair,
'I've been standing here forever, and I'd like to take the air.'
'Now you mention it, I'd love to come,' the chair at once replied.
'Why, we both have legs beneath us that we've never even tried.'

'May I keep you company?' the oaken sideboard then enquired.
'Though I am a little heavy and I fear I may get tired.
With these cups and plates and glasses in my chest, I sometimes wheeze.'
'Would you care to join us, bookcase?' And the bookcase said, 'Yes, please.'

So the furniture went strolling for an hour on the shore.
But the clock and lamp weren't able and remained there as before.
In the empty house they grumble that the others shouldn't roam.
But they know that life is like that: those who don't have legs stay home.

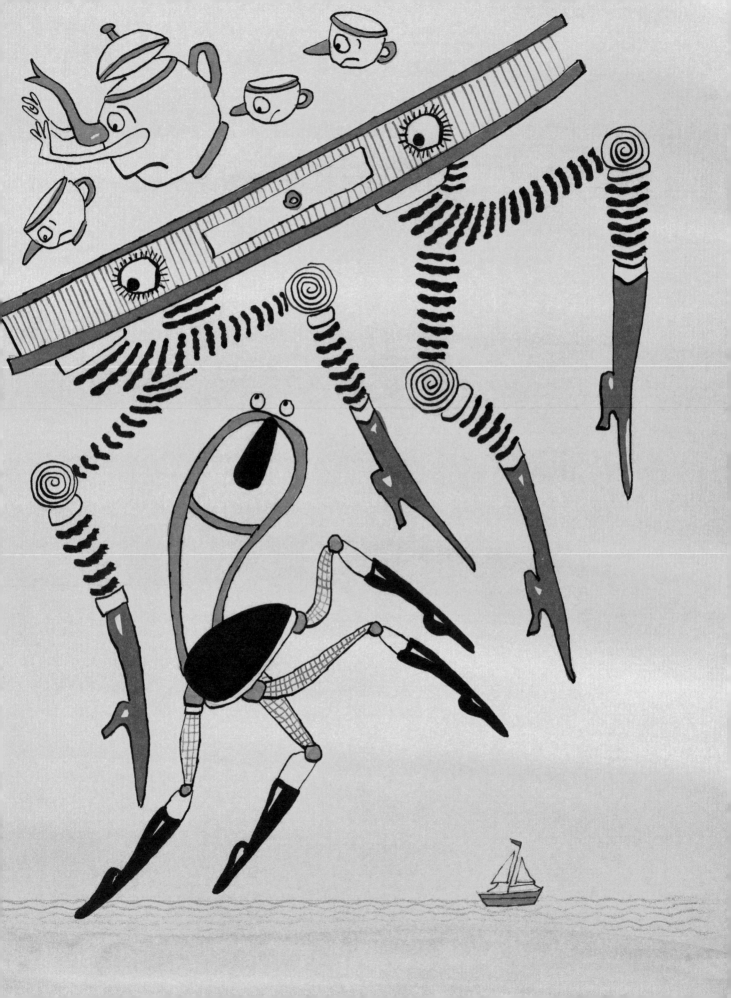

## Seven Little Eskimos

Seven little Eskimos, whose lives were very cool,
rode around in sleds all day and didn't go to school.
They rode around in little sleds without a Miss or Sir,
wrapped up warm in parkas, boots and mittens made of fur.
They lived in houses made of snow and always loved to eat
blubber, tallow, lard and fat, with frozen fish or meat.
They were happy and contented little Eskimos, all seven,
and always sang the praises of their icy Arctic heaven.

They sat down on a sheet of ice and let their legs all dangle.
They lazed and joked and fished and got their lines all in a tangle.
But then, without their noticing, that ice became a floe
and drifted off with them on top. Oh, my. Oh, dear. Oh, no!
They screamed and shouted, 'Help, help, help!' They feared their lives were over,
but two weeks later there they were: washed ashore at Dover.
Their lives were saved, that much was true, but happy they were not.
Because, you know, for Eskimos – Dover's much too hot.

They sat there crying in the sun and then they saw a van,
and heard it too – a cheerful tune – it was the ice-cream man!
He saw those seven Eskimos, and saw their consternation:
their faces red from tears and panting, furs wet with perspiration.
The ice-cream man thought deep and hard. He said, 'I tell you what.
Why don't you all climb in the back? In there, it's never hot.
For breakfast you can eat some lard, with frozen fish for tea,
and when I do my daily round, you lot can come with me.'
The Eskimos got in the back. The cold van felt like heaven.
They settled in and live there still, those Eskimos – all seven.

So if you ever go to Dover, there's a chance that you might see
an ice-cream man with seven Eskimos to keep him company.

## Aunt Sue and Uncle Steve

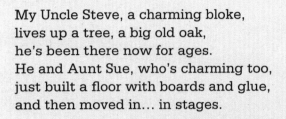

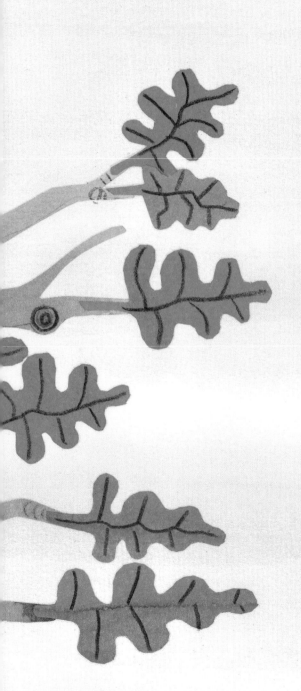

My Uncle Steve, a charming bloke,
lives up a tree, a big old oak,
he's been there now for ages.
He and Aunt Sue, who's charming too,
just built a floor with boards and glue,
and then moved in… in stages.

They sleep up there and eat up there,
it's very cosy, in the air,
except when storms are blowing.
It's quiet, large and very green,
but Aunt Sue isn't really keen –
she hates a house that's growing.

She's never really worked out how
to keep the pram parked on a bough,
it leaves her very troubled.
And now the kids are getting big,
she's scared they'll slip on leaf or twig
and all her fears have doubled.

She'd rather have a lower tree,
but Uncle Steve says, 'Goodness me,
we've got it all so pretty.
The kids just love to climb up high.
It's gorgeous sitting in the sky.
Next thing you'll miss the city.

'You say it's like a big birdcage?
These open views are all the rage!
You know I don't like bragging,
but you and I have seen the rest,
and our nest here's by far the best.
Why are you always nagging?'

There wasn't much Aunt Sue could say,
she makes her home there to this day –
it's cosy, if quite humble.
My Uncle Steve's a loving spouse,
the children climb around the house,
and no one takes a tumble.

## The Camel

There was a king who lived once in a palace on a bay,
he was quite good and noble and his beard was long and grey.
The king – *you need to know this* – kept a camel as a pet,
a lovely, little camel that he'd made a baronet.
He dressed it up in robes and cloaks and nursed it on the throne,
and all the people in that land adored it as their own.
Except for one, regrettably… Queen Mabel simply loathed it.
She loved the king, but camels, ugh! No matter how he clothed it.

'Give it a chance,' her husband smiled. 'You'll come to love it, Mabel.
And from now on the darling pet will join us at the table.'
The queen was at a total loss, she sighed, and then she said,
'Here, sweetheart, have another chop, or sausages instead.'
And the camel sat between them with a bib to catch the dribbles,
and the servants brought it soup and rice and lots of yummy nibbles.

And then, one afternoon, the king came up with something new,
'The camel will sleep in bed with us. Is that okay with you?'
'No, it is not!' the queen replied, 'I've had it up to here!
I'm sick to death of it. A queen is *not* a cameleer.
A teddy bear in bed is fine. Or some small cuddly mammal.
A cat or anything like that. But I won't have a camel!'

And then the king began to bawl. His tears poured on the floor.
He whimpered, 'No one's any fun around here anymore.'
'All right, okay,' Queen Mabel moaned. 'I'll just play second fiddle.'
And now they always sleep at night with a camel in the middle.

## Isabella Caramella

Isabella
Caramella
has to wash her baby's hair.
Isabella
Caramella
has a cuddly teddy bear
and a cuddly brown gorilla and a green-and-red checked rabbit
and she's got a crocodile – his name is Crabbit.
Isabella
Caramella
plays so sweetly in the sand.
Isabella
Caramella,
with a flower in her hand.
But if someone comes to visit and they happen to be vile,
she stops her game and whispers to her crocodile,
and her crocodile Crabbit
could do with some more lunch,
so he eats the nasty people up: *CRUNCH, CRUNCH, MUNCH!*
Like poor old Mrs Bitterbreeze, who looked on children with disdain,
and the lady in the fur coat who was such an awful pain.
And the crocodile wolfs down Mr Bowen near the trees,
down to the nasty last torn pieces of his nasty dungarees.
'Isabella
Caramella,
*where* is Mrs Bitterbreeze?
Did you perhaps
see Mr Bowen
in his purple dungarees?
Can you tell me why that woman would have left without her shoe?'
Isabella
Caramella
*doesn't have a clue.*
And she sits there
playing sweetly
with her green-and-red checked rabbit

and there beside her
in the garden
sits the crocodile Crabbit.
Isabella
Caramella
says, 'That was that!' and 'There!'
Isabella
Caramella
has to wash her baby's hair.

## The Elves and Fairies Have All Fled

My father said, my father said,
'The elves and fairies have all fled.
They used to frolic after dark
around the flowers in the park.
They'd play their games of hide and seek
and give the kitten's ear a tweak.
But now they've left the flowerbed,
the elves and fairies have all fled.'
But when I woke up in the night,
the moon had turned the grass all white.
A tiny man was standing there,
his white horse tethered to the pear.
Shim-shawl, feather and ball,
'Tis a mystery to all.

My mother sighs, my mother sighs,
'Those elves and fairies are all lies.
They don't exist. They're fantasy.
They're not out there or up a tree.
In books you find them – yes, you do –
but books are full of ballyhoo!'
That night I looked again, of course,
the man had come to sell his horse,
which bent to eat the long, green grass.
The price: three buttons made of brass.
Shim-shawl, feather and ball,
'Tis a mystery to all.

My father slept, my mother slept,
as through the garden gate I stepped.
I climbed up on the horse's back
and rode it down a gleaming track.
No one knows that I went there
and saw the fairies everywhere,
and no one knows I swung up high
on spider webs hung from the sky,
and no one knows that it's great fun
playing hide-and-seek with a fairy's son
and leapfrog with a laughing elf
and hop-scotch with the king himself.
Shim-shawl, feather and ball,
'Tis a mystery to all.

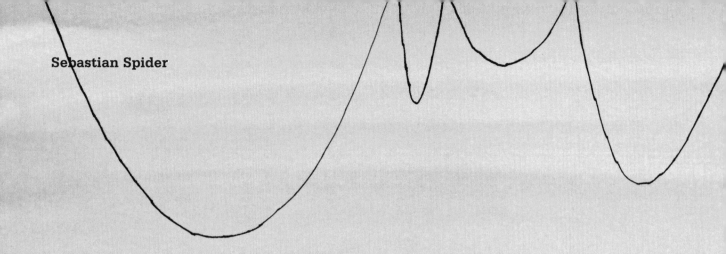

**Sebastian Spider**

This is poor Sebastian S.
He got into an awful mess.

*LISTEN!*

Sebastian stated with a grin,
'It's strange. I'm not myself today,
I feel an urge from deep within
to spin a web without delay.'

All the other spiders cried,
'Oh, Sebastian! No, Sebastian!
Please, Sebastian, don't be so silly.
In wintertime we sleep and hide.
No one makes webs when it's this chilly.'

But Sebastian just replied,
'Webs can be small and hard to find –
if it's too cold, I'll go inside,
and sneak one in behind a blind.'

All the other spiders cried,
'Oh, Sebastian! No, Sebastian!
Please, Sebastian, don't make a fuss!
It's much too dangerous inside.
There's danger for the likes of us.'

Sebastian stubbornly insisted,
'This Urge of mine is far too strong.'

The other spiders still resisted,
'Inside that house, you won't live long...'
Oh, oh, oh, Sebastian S!
He got into an awful mess.

An open window – he slipped inside.
Stubborn, yes, but walking tall!
All the other spiders cried,
'There goes Sebastian, Urge and all!'

*SHORT PAUSE*

A little later, without pardon,
this simple message reached the garden,
'A murderer was in the room.
Sebastian S. just met the broom.'

**Ghosts at the Castle**

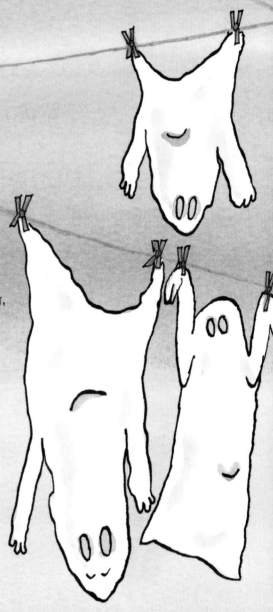

There is an old castle
called Keep of Le Grâsle
that's haunted at night.
It could be just one ghost,
it could be a hundred,
but all of them white.

Sometimes they're keening and sometimes they're groaning,
sometimes they're leaning on moonbeams and moaning,
down there by the pond where they ripple the water,
and then the gamekeeper will say to his daughter,
'Jane,
them ghosts be back again.'

But four times a year,
no more and no less
(explains the countess),
they float through the door
and lie down right here
on the cold laundry floor.

Then the dry-cleaning man
comes by in his van
to pick up the lot
and wash them that day,
and like it or not
the countess has to pay.

And later that night they'll be groaning and sighing,
and flitting and fluttering and flapping and flying,
down there by the pond where they ripple the water,
and then the gamekeeper will say to his daughter,
'Jane,
them ghosts be white again.'
And then his daughter will say – most distressed –
'Yes, and they've even been pressed.'

## Macbeth the Cat

Fancy that! Macbeth the cat,
playing the aristocrat.
Like an upper-crust feline,
he has gone to town to dine.
Has Macbeth got so much money?
Here's the bit that's really funny…
Shhh! He borrowed fifty bucks
from a big Muscovy duck.

The waitresses all call him sir,
spoken with a throaty purr.
The place is called Ye Olde Catte House,
specialised in sautéed mouse,
and the well-fed lady cats
always take some cream with that.
Macbeth sits down and, very posh,
says, 'Waiter, what you got to nosh?'

'I suggest,' says waiter cat,
'that you start with roasted rat,
followed by a fishy fillet,
à la meow in our best skillet.
Dessert, of course, comes after that.'
'Purrfect,' says Macbeth the cat.
Oh, Macbeth can eat a lot.
He scoffs it down while it's still hot.

Who arrives then suddenly?
That angry duck from Muscovy!
'Look at this,' the duck explodes,
'First he comes and borrows loads,
then pigs out to his heart's content.
Now pay me back! Plus ten percent!'
But Macbeth the cat escapes
by climbing up the Catte House drapes.

And the duck thinks sadly, 'Yeah,
I can't follow him up there.'
That's why he immediately
goes back home to Muscovy.

One thing you can learn from that:
Don't lend money to a cat.

## Sir Ironsides

There once was a knight known as Sir Ironsides,
he lived long ago and was known far and wide.
He'd slay you a dragon for a kiss and a rose –
a rate that's outdated as anyone knows.
Courageous and noble was Sir Ironsides!
But when it got dark he was so terrified!

He'd lie there in terror until it grew light,
scared stiff of the things that go bump in the night!
To raise up his spirits before things got worse,
he'd try to compose an encouraging verse
and to start himself off he'd invariably say,
'What are some of the great deeds that I've done today?
One maiden rescued,
five dragons killed dead!
So why am I lying here
quaking in bed?'

And then, when the sun was back up in the sky,
he'd vanquish those dragons as if they were flies,
so brave and courageous was Sir Ironsides.
But when it got dark he was just terrified,
and then he'd start frantically rhyming away.
'What are some of the nice things that I've done today?
I galloped my horse
and I ate a big spread,
I talked to my wife
while she massaged my head,
So why am I lying here
shaking in bed?'

By one in the morning it gets out of hand!
By then the poor knight is completely unmanned
and whimpering softly at each peep or creak
and lying there mumbling, his hands to his cheeks,
'One dragon rescued,
five maidens killed dead…
Am I hearing right?
What was that I just said?
I galloped my wife
and I ate a big bed…
I talked to my horse while it massaged my head…
I'm getting confused, it's such misery,
I'm scared of the dark!
Who'll come rescue me?
            *Mummmmmy!*

## The Tabby Cat

'Wet and freezing! Wet and freezing!' said the tabby cat.
'Wipe your feet, please. Wipe your feet, please, on the mat, mat, mat.
    Hello, Teddy.
    Here already?
Raining steady! Raining steady!
And the steady drops are falling, "Splat, splat, splat."
Wipe your feet please,' said the tabby cat.

'May I come in?' asked the teddy with a little bow.
'I'm quite done in. I'm quite done in. May I come in now?
    I'm in need of care and nursing.
    Chill blains on my toes are hurting.
Every step I take my feet go, "Ow, ow, ow."
Please,' said Teddy, 'may I come in now?'

'In the kitchen, in the kitchen,' said the tabby cat.
'Are they itching? Are they itching? Oh, I do hate that.
    I feel sorry for you, Teddy,
    But I've got a bandage ready
and now I'll wet that bandage at the tap, tap, tap.
    And that's that,' said the cat,
    'They're wrapped up,' said the cat.
    'That is that,' said the tabby cat.

**The Fairy Failure**

A mother fairy long ago
preferred her kids to be 'just so'.
The kids in question were two girls,
with shining wings and golden curls.
The oldest one was sheer perfection
and had a fairy's white complexion.
The second girl, though just as graceful,
was kind of freckly – she had a face full.

Her mother did what she could do,
she washed her cheeks with catkin dew,
she dabbed her brow with tiger's milk
and bandaged it with magic silk,
she dipped her in a rain-wet lily –
it made the freckles no less silly.

'Oh daughter dear,' her mother sighed,
'your freckles have just multiplied!
As fairies go' – and here she started talking faster –
'you're hopeless, you're an absolute disaster.

'Go now to old King Scarabee
and say, "*Oh please, Your Majesty,
I beg you for your kind protection,
I'm a fairy with a rare complexion.*"

'With any luck King Scarabee,
who's known for his philanthropy,
will help a sad and freckly fairy –
he might employ you in his dairy.'

The fairy left without delay,
she slept at night and flew by day,
and muttered softly on the way,
'*I beg you... please... Your Majesty...
protect you for your... kind... connection...
I'm a fairy with a rare complexion.*'

She reached the town all worn and wan,
and feeling scared and woebegone.
The king himself came to the door
and said, 'What can I do you for?'

And very, very timidly,
she stammered, '*Please... Your Majesty...*
*protect you with your fair... complexion...*
*I'm a raree for your kind collection.*'

'I'm fair, indeed,' the king replied,
'I bathe in milk, please come inside.
Are you acquainted with Queen Mary?
You know, I've never met a raree.'

He clicked his fingers in the air
and all at once his court was there:
'This is a raree,
a creature most extraordinairy,
give her some cake and some chocolate too,
give her some clothes and a room with a view.'

The fairy now lives happily,
a guest of old King Scarabee.
She's not a milkmaid in the dairy –
Oh no! She's now the Royal Raree.

She has a golden bedroom suite,
and golden slippers on her feet,
and dukes and princes, lords and all
are gladly at her beck and call.
If nothing else this goes to show:
*A total misfit as a fairy*
*can be a big hit as a raree.*
That kind of thing is nice to know.

## Are you joking, Mrs Keller?

'Are you joking, Mrs Keller?
Keeping bears down in your cellar?
Keeping bears here in a residential street?
If they were rabbits I'd ignore them
and pretend I never saw them,
but these are bears with teeth and claws
        and hairy feet!'

'Mr Reeves, now just you listen,
I don't need to ask permission.
My bears are really no concern of yours.

'Go and check them if you'd rather,
but I got them from my father
and I love them from their ears down to
        their paws.'

'Well, in such a situation,
I must go down to the station.
The police will know exactly what to do!'
'Mr Reeves, you'd better listen,
because if that's a firm decision,
I might need to set my seven bears on you!

'They are growling. Can you hear them?
You can't miss it when you're near them.'
Grrr! Grrr! Grrr! Grrr! Rowl! Rowl! Grrr!

'Mr Reeves, now that you've listened,
are you sure of your position?'
'Um, not really, Mrs Keller, maybe not...

'Well, I'll be going, Mrs Keller,
I'll just pick up my umbrella,
and I hope you have a great time with your bears.'
'Oh, Mr Reeves, you needn't worry,
but I see you're in a hurry,
so, goodbye, and do be careful on the stairs.'
        Grrrrrr!

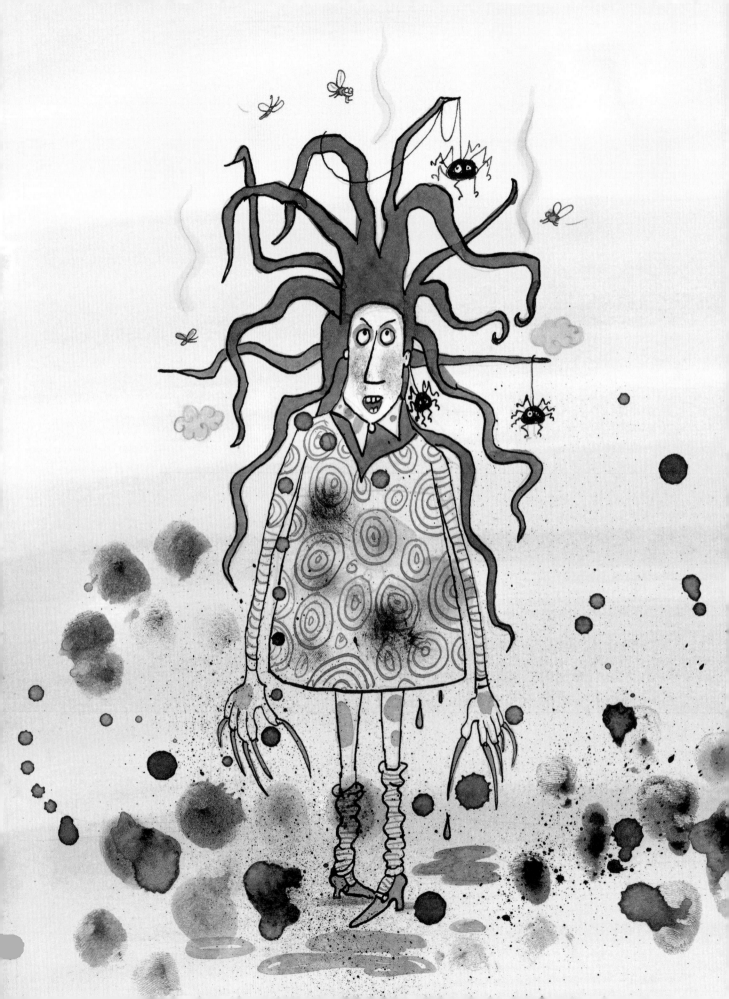

## Belinda Hated Getting Clean...

Belinda Beronda, from somewhere near Flushing,
was not keen on washing and not fond of brushing.
She was an inveterate cleanliness-hater,
and always postponed her baths until later.
Her bodily odour grew stronger and stronger,
and her hair and her nails grew longer and longer.
Belinda was filthy, a terrible fright.
She looked like a pig, a horrible sight.
And when her mother finally came home,
with soap and shampoo and a brush and a comb,
Belinda just started to scream, shriek and blub,
as if she was going to drown in the tub.
Her mother – by now, at the end of her tether –
gave in and shouted, 'Stay dirty for ever!
But if that's what you want, you just walk out that door,
but I won't be your mother anymore!'
And that filthy little Belinda Beronda
took off up the street and started to wander
the highways and byways all over the land,
getting grubby and covered with mud, dirt and sand,
with grimy smudges all over her face.
The more she avoided a bathroom or scrubbery,
the more she began to resemble some shrubbery.
Grass started growing on her shoes and her clothes,
it covered one leg, then slowly rose,
until she was totally, thoroughly hid
and no one could see that she was a kid.
And then the roots grew into the ground,
and fixed her in place like a tree on a mound.
Birds came and built little nests on her sleeves,
and slowly she grew her own branches and leaves.
A nightmare, but true, you can take it from me,
Belinda Beronda turned into a tree.

So now you know. Little cleanliness-haters
end up as trees... sooner or later.

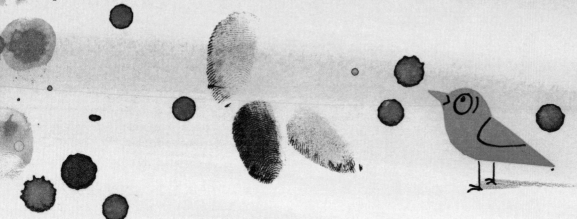

**Aunty Jo**

When Aunty Jo of Camden Town
came downstairs in her dressing gown,
at half past six one morning,
she got an awfully large surprise,
and stopped and stared and rubbed her eyes.
It made her stop her yawning!

She felt like flopping on the chair,
but couldn't 'cause a deer was there.
She yelled and shouted, 'Psst!' and 'Shoo!'
and grabbed a plate, which she then threw,
the deer just looked up blinking

and listened to the radio,
while poor, unhappy Aunty Jo
was desperately thinking,
and feeling sad and awful queer,
for on the sofa sat a deer.

She knew she needed someone's aid
and quickly called the fire brigade
and the police inspector.
The people came from near and far
and looked and shouted, 'Ooh!' and 'Ah!'
and offered to protect her.

'Well strike me dead,' said Uncle Fred,
'The sofa's now a reindeer bed!'
Though no one had the slightest clue
of what to say or what to do,
the deer seemed most contented

and sat so still that Aunty Jo,
who'd longed to have it up and go,
quite suddenly relented.
She let it stay and in the end
the deer became a dear, dear friend,
who Jo loves like a brother.

And now she uses all its prongs
to hang her ladles, pots and tongs –
a pan rack like no other.
And Aunty Jo says, 'Wonderful!
It's even good for winding wool.
I never lose a spoon or knife
and the deer now has a goal in life.'

**Betty Snap**

There used to be a little girl and she looked very cute,
she wore a tartan jacket and had golden curls to boot,
but no one, no one, no one in the world was able to love her
and when they saw her coming all the people just took cover:

*SHE SNAPPED!*

She snapped at her own mother and she snapped at Uncle Giles,
she even visited the zoo to snap at crocodiles.
She snapped at Pete the veggie man and Joe the local baker,
she'd snap at people anywhere her mother cared to take her.
She snapped at dogs and cats and all the teachers at her school,
and everybody everywhere thought she was horrible.
And no one liked her, not at all. They wished she'd shut her trap.
'And if she doesn't,' someone said, 'We'll call her Betty Snap.'

There came a day when Betty rode her scooter down the street,
everyone had gone inside, it was almost time to eat,
there was just one old, old lady walking slowly with a stick,
and Betty Snap began to shout, 'Get out of the way! And quick!
Can't you see I'm riding here? Move it! Go, go, go!'
That wasn't very friendly of the little so-and-so.

That lady took a good long look at Betty on her scooter,
then mumbled, 'Hocus pocus, piggious porkus, substitute her...'
She waved her magic wand and her expression turned quite scary,
because, you see, that lady was a rather famous fairy,
and she'd decided quickly that no one would give a fig,
if she transformed this kid into a scooter-riding pig.

When Betty's mother called her in – 'Come on, it's time for tea!' –
she didn't look upon that pig with equanimity.
It rode up on the scooter dressed in Betty's tartan jacket,
and Betty's mother felt an urge to grab the broom and whack it.
But wait! Was that her little girl? That nasty, smelly thing?
She'd always been a pain, but this was too embarrassing!

Fortunately Betty's Aunt Eliza was there too.
She said, 'A fairy's work, that is, and I know what to do.'
Eliza was acquainted with all the local fairies,
she knew the one from London and the one from Buenos Aires.
And Eliza was decisive, she'd never waste a minute,
she grabbed the pig, then stopped a cab and immediately jumped in it.

'Oh, fairy dear,' said Aunt Eliza, 'This is Betty Snap.
I know that she was mean and rude, but after this mishap,
she'll be a different girl. Won't she?' And the pig let out a squeal.
'Please, please, please, change her back. We'll be so grateful. We'll, um, we'll—'
'Oh, all right,' said the fairy, as she gave her wand a wave.
'I'll change her to a girl again, but make sure she behaves!'

And Betty was a girl again, a girl who never snapped!
With just a curly tail left and that was kind of apt:
a tail to remind her, poking out beneath her skirt.
The other kids could see it and their laughter must have hurt,
but luckily it soon fell off. (It took a month or two.)
They kept it as a souvenir. That seemed the thing to do.

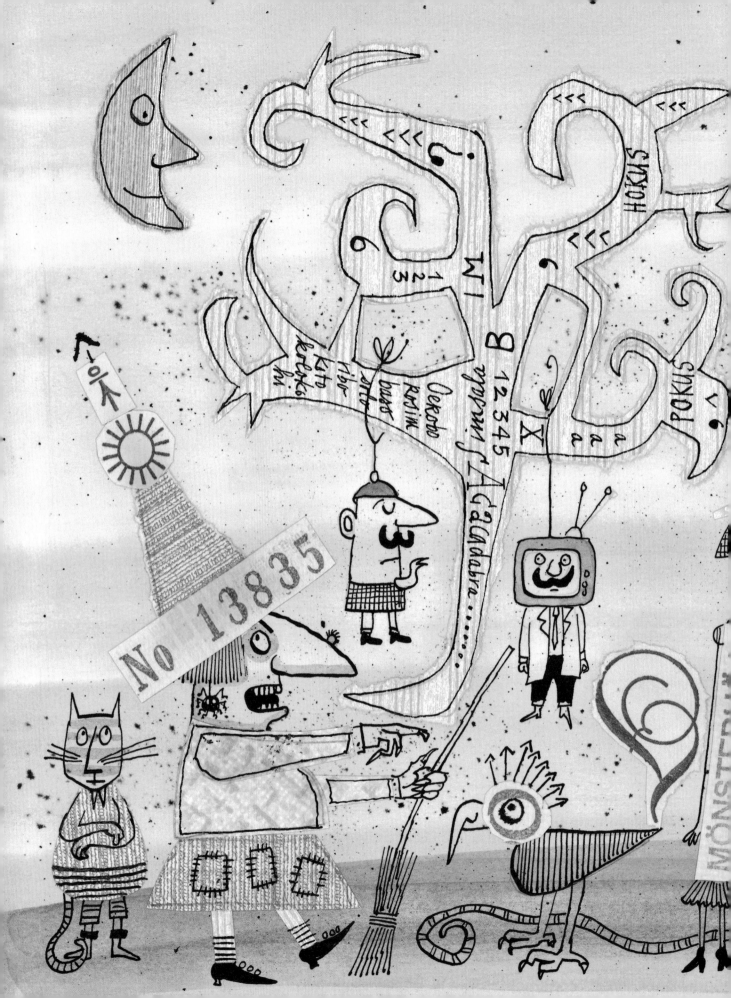

## The Witch from Saddlestitch

This is the witch from Saddlestitch,
she loves it when it's raining
The things she does are just too rich,
and everyone's complaining,
'Oh, what a witch,
what an 'orrible witch,
she just does it to taunt us.
That nasty witch from Saddlestitch,
how much longer will she haunt us?'

*On Sunday she takes the baronet*
*and turns him into a TV set.*

*On Monday she doesn't do too much,*
*but flies around to keep in touch.*

*On Tuesday she eats a teacher up,*
*then soaks her dentures in a cup.*

*On Wednesday she takes the TV set*
*and turns it into a baronet.*
*(The joy is over in a wink –*
*turns out the fellow's on the blink.)*

*On Thursday she takes the ladies' choir,*
*and makes them all as thin as wire.*

*On Friday she bites the registrar*
*then rolls him up like a big cigar.*

*On Saturday she has three baths,*
*and splashes while she sits and laughs,*
*and says, 'I bet they din't like that!'*
*and, otherwise, plays with her cat.*

This is the witch from Saddlestitch,
she loves it when it's raining.
The mayor has got a nervous twitch,
her tricks are very draining.
'Oh, what a witch,
what an 'orrible witch,
no one here can stand her.
That awful witch from Saddlestitch,
why ain't someone banned her?'

**The Whim-Wham Giant**

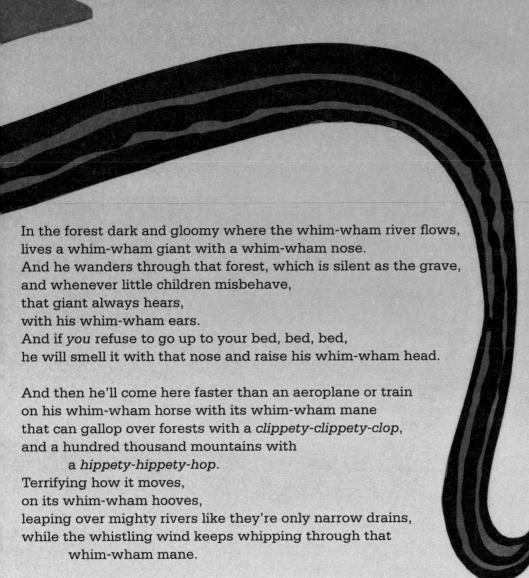

In the forest dark and gloomy where the whim-wham river flows,
lives a whim-wham giant with a whim-wham nose.
And he wanders through that forest, which is silent as the grave,
and whenever little children misbehave,
that giant always hears,
with his whim-wham ears.
And if *you* refuse to go up to your bed, bed, bed,
he will smell it with that nose and raise his whim-wham head.

And then he'll come here faster than an aeroplane or train
on his whim-wham horse with its whim-wham mane
that can gallop over forests with a *clippety-clippety-clop*,
and a hundred thousand mountains with
　　　a *hippety-hippety-hop*.
Terrifying how it moves,
on its whim-wham hooves,
leaping over mighty rivers like they're only narrow drains,
while the whistling wind keeps whipping through that
　　　whim-wham mane.

Naughty children, please take heed. Naughty children,
　　　please beware
of the whim-wham giant with the whim-wham hair,
and if *you* don't go to bed and if *you're* not good,
that giant will smack your bottom with a great big
　　　piece of wood!
　　　And not ordinary wood...
　　　Oh, no!
　　　*Whim-wham wood!*

## Little Princess Annabel

There used to be a princess by the name of Annabel,
and now I'll tell her story, so you'd better listen well.
She had the cutest little plaits, a gold crown on her head,
she had a great big bedroom with a diamond-studded bed,
the king and queen would come and tell her bedtime fairy tales
and then she'd get a lullaby from two white nightingales,
and mostly she was good and sweet… at meals, at work and play,
and everybody loved her so… *except* on Saturday,
because always, always, once a week, that lovely royal child
got prickly, grumpy, mean and loud, unbearable and wild.
She'd smash the plates and throw the chairs, and yell and scream and shout,
and make the kind of noise you'd get from letting lions out!

The king and queen conferred and said, 'Perhaps we'd better act.
This can't go on. Enough's enough. She's really lacking tact.
She bit the butler on the butt. The maids are growing thinner.
We need to write and ask Kazamm the Sorcerer to dinner.'

Kazamm the Sorcerer! Of course! He's such a wiz at magic.
If he can't help her, no one can, and that would be too tragic!
He flew right in next Saturday with a little loop-the-loop,
and joined them at the table for some vermicelli soup.
'Well,' said Kazamm the Sorcerer, 'How are you, my dear princess?
Do you enjoy geography? And are you good at chess?'
She grabbed her spoon and glared at him, the charming little tot,
then hurled it at him soup and all. The soup was boiling hot!
The poor, poor man! His hair was full of manky vermicelli.
What a nasty, horrid, trouble-making, naughty Annabelly!

The queen choked back a tear, the king frowned and gave a little cough,
and then they used their royal napkins to dry the wizard off.
'You see? Exactly as we said. You can tell it's Saturday.
The poor dear is so prickly when she doesn't get her way!'
'*The poor dear is so prickly*?!' yelled Kazamm the Sorcerer.
'If the little brat wants *prickly*, then I'm the man for her.'
He quickly waved his magic wand and said a magic spell
and – *Poof!* – a hedgehog was sitting there instead of Annabel.
The sorcerer flew out the window and off into the night,
the king and queen were both struck dumb, and overcome by fright,
they cried and cried and cried and cried, with voices growing hoarser,
then gave poor Princess Annabel some warm milk in a saucer.

She was an ordinary hedgehog, no matter how well-bred,
but just like any other night, they took her up to bed.
The king and queen went up to tell her bedtime fairy tales
and then she got a lullaby from two white nightingales…

And Kazamm? He flew straight home. He ran a bath and lit a candle.
He searched and found the scrubbing brush with the extended handle,
then washed off all the vermicelli, every last wet thread,
and as he washed it off, he found he got a *cooler* head.
He sighed and said to himself, 'I really was a little mean.
Is it too late to fix it up? It's almost 10:15!'

He donned his wings and – making sure he wasn't seen on the way –
flew quickly to the window where the hedgehog-child lay.
And who was there next morning in that diamond-studded bed
with the cutest little ash-blonde plaits and a gold crown on her head?
Not a royal little hedgehog, no, but Princess Annabel.
The king and queen just stood there mumbling, 'Goodness, well, well, well…'

And best of all: that princess is lovely now the whole week through.
Really? Can it be true? Even Saturdays? …Then too!

## The Robbers and the Moon

There were three greedy robbers who had made a cave their base.
It wasn't fun to live there, it was more a storage place,
with boxes full of diamonds and with cases full of gold,
with silver, rugs and tapestries – though they were flecked with mould.
Those robbers weren't contented, no, their lives were not ideal.
They longed to go out robbing, but there was nothing left to steal.
They scratched their heads and racked their brains, 'Ain't there nothin' we forgot?'
But when they looked around them they could see they'd robbed the lot.

The cave was dark and gloomy, but the moon shone through a chink,
a shining perfect silver moon. That made the robbers think…
The moon! Why hadn't they thought of that before? They'd steal the moon!
They'd go and get it straightaway and not a night too soon.
They started stealing steeples, 'cause they're always nice and high,
and when they had three of the things they thought they'd have a try.
They stacked the steeples one on one and climbed like three baboons…
Those robbers were determined that, that night, they'd steal the moon.

Two robbers closed their eyes because they'd started to feel dizzy.
The third one shouted, 'Cowards!' and climbed higher in a tizzy.
He grabbed the moon and pulled it down, waving to his friends.
They shouted 'Careful! Hold it tight!' and he started to descend.
The moon was smooth and slippery and it weighed about a ton.
It slipped right through his fingers, there was nothing to be done!
The moon fell like a lead balloon. They listened for a crash,
but it came down in the river and they heard a mighty splash.
With one last hiss: hiss-SISS! It sank for all eternity.
Which makes it fair to say, the moon was clearly hisstory.

I'm glad to say there is a group (I don't know if you know this)
of very old professors, a commission, and its name is
The Grand Commission for the Moon and All Things Lunar.
They looked up and saw that it was gone. They should have noticed sooner!

'The moon's not there!' they cried. 'It isn't hanging on its hook.
No moon! That's terrible. Just think how stupid we'll look!'
Luckily the chairman had an old moon under his bed.
So quickly they decided to hang that one up instead.

The robbers crept into their cave, their plans in disarray.
They're scared to come back out again and sit there to this day.
And now you know the truth of it. The moon you see up there
is not the real moon after all. It's really just a spare.

## The Train Was Stuck

The train awaits, the train awaits,
the train to Fort McMurray.
The people jostle through the gates
and hurry, hurry, hurry.
'Goodbye, goodbye, it's time to go.'
They sit down in their places,
and just in time, the whistle blows.
Relief on all their faces.
'We're all on board. What luck! What luck!
But, huh, what's this? The train is stuck!'

'What's wrong? What's up? What's happening?
It's almost gone three thirty.'
Nobody seems to know a thing.
The guard looks very shirty.
The stationmaster seems upset,
but also scared… How curious.
The engine-driver's wet with sweat,
and looking simply furious.
If he calms down perhaps he might
explain just why the train's stuck tight.

The engine-driver shouts, 'Explain?!'
His anger now increases.
'The engine of my lovely train
is scattered all in pieces.
Look! Here's a bit and there's a bit
of my fantastic engine…
I'm so angry, I could spit.'
And then he turns to whingin'.
'How could this have happened to us?'
But, look! Who's that? Is that young Gus?

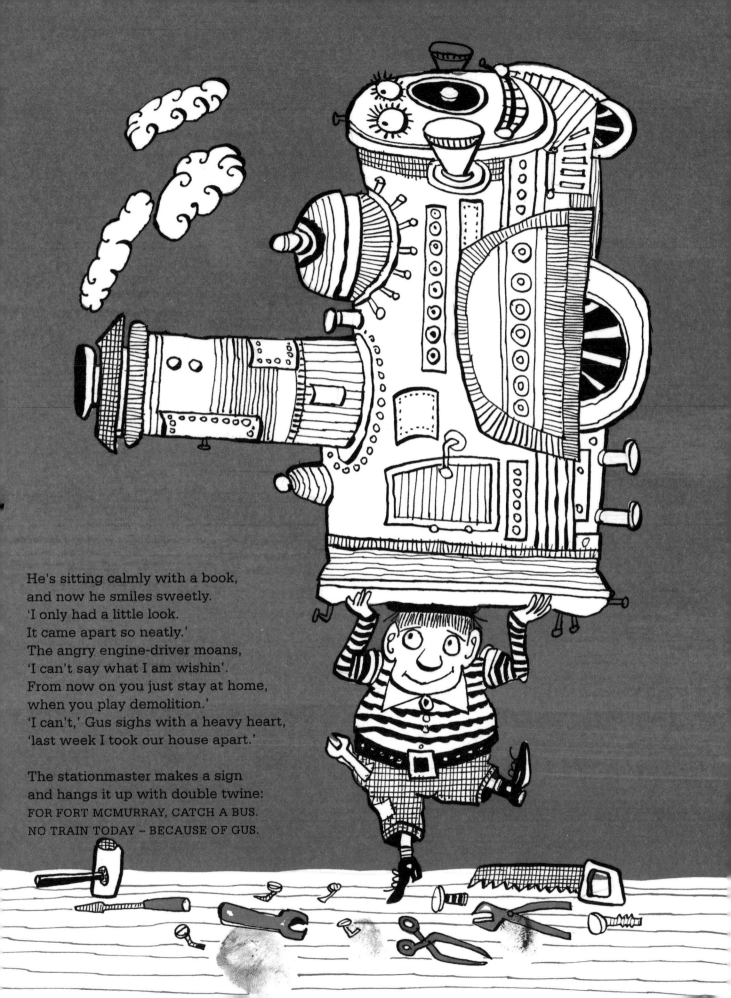

He's sitting calmly with a book,
and now he smiles sweetly.
'I only had a little look.
It came apart so neatly.'
The angry engine-driver moans,
'I can't say what I am wishin'.
From now on you just stay at home,
when you play demolition.'
'I can't,' Gus sighs with a heavy heart,
'last week I took our house apart.'

The stationmaster makes a sign
and hangs it up with double twine:
FOR FORT MCMURRAY, CATCH A BUS.
NO TRAIN TODAY – BECAUSE OF GUS.

## The Naughty Children's Home

On the road that leads here from Rome,
you'll find the Naughty Children's Home.
One hundred kids are living there,
the kind of kids who just don't care.
None of them are good or quiet,
in that home it's one big riot.
Kids scream, 'Yah!' and kids scream, 'Hoo!'
Isn't there anyone who says what to do?
      Yes, there is.

Mr Jonathan B. Weerd
has a nasty, bushy beard.
All day long, like a cat in a cage,
Mr Weerd is in a rage.
'Silence,' he cries in a voice that's a screech,
'I'll give you all a hundred lines each!'
But a hundred kids just shout back, 'Boo!'
Isn't that a shocking thing to do?
      Yes, it is.

Every morning you can see
kids behave atrociously,
running around and pulling the beard
of Mr Jonathan B. Weerd,
climbing trees and doing bad things,
yelling and whooping and screaming like mad things.
Hey, wouldn't you like to live there too?
Wouldn't that Home be perfect for you?
      Ye… Surely not?

# Patterson Pepps

Patterson Pepps climbed up the steps
with a sugar cube from the table
and the giraffe came out of its stable.
'Hi, Giraffe,' said Patterson Pepps,
'D'you know what Mummy gave me?
Bright red boots for when it's rainy!'
'Can it be true?' said the giraffe.
'Patterson, Patterson, what a laugh.'

'Oh, Giraffe,' said Patterson Pepps.
'I've got lots more I can tell you.
There's three letters I can spell too:
a b c – that's clever of me!
And I can almost tie my laces!
And I can draw all kinds of faces!'
'Goodness me,' said the giraffe,
'boy, oh boy, that's not by halves.'

'Hey, Giraffe,' said Patterson Pepps,
'do you think I could try riding
on your neck and then try sliding?
Just once to see, if you'll let me.
Sliding down onto the zoo floor
shouldn't make my bottom too sore.'
'Climb on up,' said the giraffe,
'Climb on up but don't be rough.'

Patterson Pepps climbed off the steps
with a scary, great big step.
On the neck of the giraffe,
little Patterson Pepps pushed off.
Whoosh, and with a mighty wail,
he went whizzing to the tail.
            Bang!
            Ow!!

'Bye, Giraffe,' said Patterson Pepps.
'Monday I'll be back here with my steps.'